MW00614319

A Solution to

THE MARRIAGE MESS

By Jack T. Chick

Illustrated by
Fred Carter

Chick Publications
P.O. Box 3500
Ontario, Calif. 91761-1019 USA

MY DEEPEST APPRECIATION TO . . . . .

> MY LOVELY **WIFE,** LOLA LYNN CHICK
> PASTOR JAMES L. FRANKLIN
> DR. LLOYD T. ANDERSON
> AND MY GREAT STAFF FOR ALL THEIR HELP.

ALSO A SPECIAL THANKS TO . . . . . .

> JOANN CASH YATES, WHO READ THE DISCARDED
> MANUSCRIPT OF "THE MARRIAGE MESS" AND
> TALKED ME INTO PUBLISHING IT.

PUBLISHED BY:
CHICK PUBLICATIONS
PO BOX 3500, ONTARIO, CALIF. 91761-1019 USA
TEL: (909) 987-0771
FAX: (909) 941-8128
WEB: WWW.CHICK.COM
EMAIL: POSTMASTER@CHICK.COM

PRINTED IN THE UNITED STATES OF AMERICA

ISBN: 9780758914477

WHEN GOD SAID TO EVE . . . "WHAT IS THIS THAT THOU HAST DONE?" (GENESIS 3:13) HE ALREADY KNEW THE HORRIFYING CHAIN REACTION OF PROBLEMS THAT THEIR ACT OF REBELLION HAD CAUSED.

WARS, TORTURE, PERVERSION, DESPAIR, SUFFERING, LONELINESS, HATE, DISEASE, FEAR, SICKNESS, CONFUSION, DEATH AND HEARTBREAK SPREAD ACROSS HUMANITY LIKE GIANT SPIDERWEBS ENTANGLING ALL OF OUR LIVES.

TODAY, CHRISTIAN HOMES ARE BEING BATTERED BY THE FORCES OF DARKNESS.

IT WOULD BE THE HEIGHT OF PRESUMPTION TO SAY THAT THIS BOOK HAS ANSWERS TO MOST OF THE COMPLEX PROBLEMS IN OUR HOMES; BUT, IF ONE LITTLE RAY OF TRUTH COULD IMPROVE YOUR FAMILY LIFE, THEN THIS LITTLE BOOK WAS WELL WORTH WHILE.

J.T.C.

CONTENTS

CHAPTER ONE

THE FRIENDLY FANATIC

7

8

10

12

13

15

*"A MAN'S GIFT MAKETH ROOM FOR HIM..." PROVERBS 18:16

17

18

19

20

21

CHAPTER TWO

SOUP'S ON!

GOOD MORNING, HELEN ... I'M SORRY I OVERSLEPT ... THE TIME CHANGES ON MY FLIGHT FROM AFRICA GOT MY SLEEPING HABITS ALL MESSED UP!

HUMMPH! ... I'VE BEEN WAITING TO COOK YOUR BREAKFAST _ALL_ MORNING. NOW I'M LATE FOR MY HAIR DRESSER! . . . SO _YOU'RE_ GOING TO HAVE TO MAKE YOUR _OWN_ BREAKFAST ... THE HOUSE IS A MESS, BUT I'M TOO BUSY!

I'LL SEE YOU LATE THIS AFTERNOON!

23

24

"WHETHER THEREFORE YE EAT, OR DRINK, OR WHATSOEVER YE DO, DO ALL TO THE GLORY OF GOD." 1 CORINTHIANS 10:31

25

"AND WHATSOEVER YE DO IN WORD OR DEED, DO ALL IN THE NAME OF THE LORD JESUS, GIVING THANKS TO GOD AND THE FATHER BY HIM." COLOSSIANS 3:17

26

29

31

32

*JOHN 21:4-13 **JOHN 1:1, 2, 3, & 14

33

35

36

37

38

39

41

42

CHAPTER THREE

THE UGLY TRUTH!

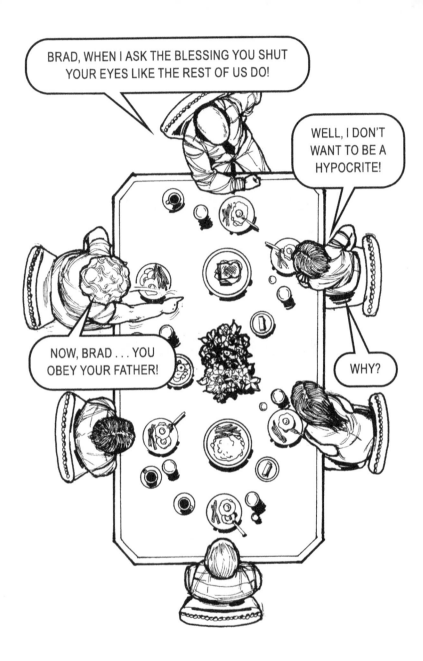

44

46

47

48

49

LATER THAT DAY

IS MRS. MILLER HOME?

NO, SHE'S AT CHURCH . . . IS THERE A PROBLEM?

YES, SIR. WE MADE A DRUG RAID... AND UNCOVERED 50 POUNDS OF MARIJUANA... WE FOUND BRAD VISITING THE DEALERS.

INSTEAD OF TAKING HIM TO JUVENILE HALL, WE BROUGHT HIM HOME!

PLEASE COME IN, GENTLEMEN!

51

53

55

*"FOR WE MUST ALL APPEAR BEFORE THE JUDGMENT SEAT OF CHRIST;
THAT EVERY ONE MAY RECEIVE THE THINGS DONE IN HIS BODY,
ACCORDING TO THAT HE HATH DONE, WHETHER IT BE GOOD OR BAD."

57

IT WILL BE A DIFFERENT STORY WHEN WE STAND BEFORE HIM AND SEE OUR REWARDS* GO DOWN THE TUBES.

THE LORD JESUS WILL SHOW US HOW EVERY ACT WE DID INFLUENCED THE PEOPLE WATCHING US, FOR EITHER HEAVEN OR HELL.

"FOR OTHER FOUNDATION CAN NO MAN LAY THAN THAT IS LAID, WHICH IS JESUS CHRIST. NOW IF ANY MAN BUILD UPON THIS FOUNDATION GOLD, SILVER, PRECIOUS STONES, WOOD, HAY, STUBBLE; EVERY MAN'S WORK SHALL BE MADE MANIFEST: FOR THE DAY SHALL DECLARE IT, BECAUSE IT SHALL BE REVEALED BY FIRE; AND THE FIRE SHALL TRY EVERY MAN'S WORK OF WHAT SORT IT IS. IF ANY MAN'S WORK ABIDE WHICH HE HATH BUILT THEREUPON, HE SHALL RECEIVE A REWARD. IF ANY MAN'S WORK SHALL BE BURNED, HE SHALL SUFFER LOSS: BUT HE HIMSELF SHALL BE SAVED; YET SO AS BY FIRE." 1 CORINTHIANS 3:11-15

60

61

62

63

64

65

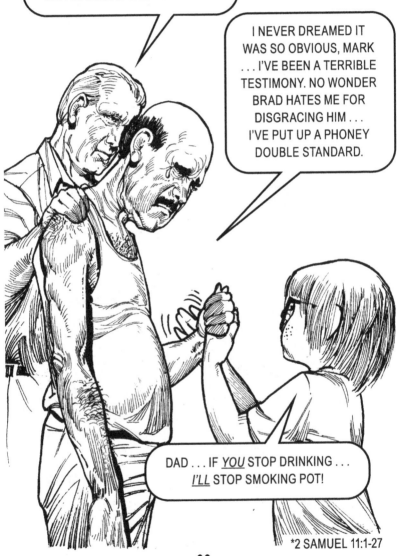

*2 SAMUEL 11:1-27

67

CHAPTER FOUR

MURDER?

69

70

71

73

74

75

MEANWHILE DOWN AT THE OFFICE
MR. MILLER . . . I'M HAVING PROBLEMS WITH MY DAUGHTER . . . SHE'S SANDY'S AGE . . . IS SANDY REBELLIOUS?
NOT AT ALL . . . YOU SEE, WE RAISED HER THE RIGHT WAY!
NK MILLER

77

78

79

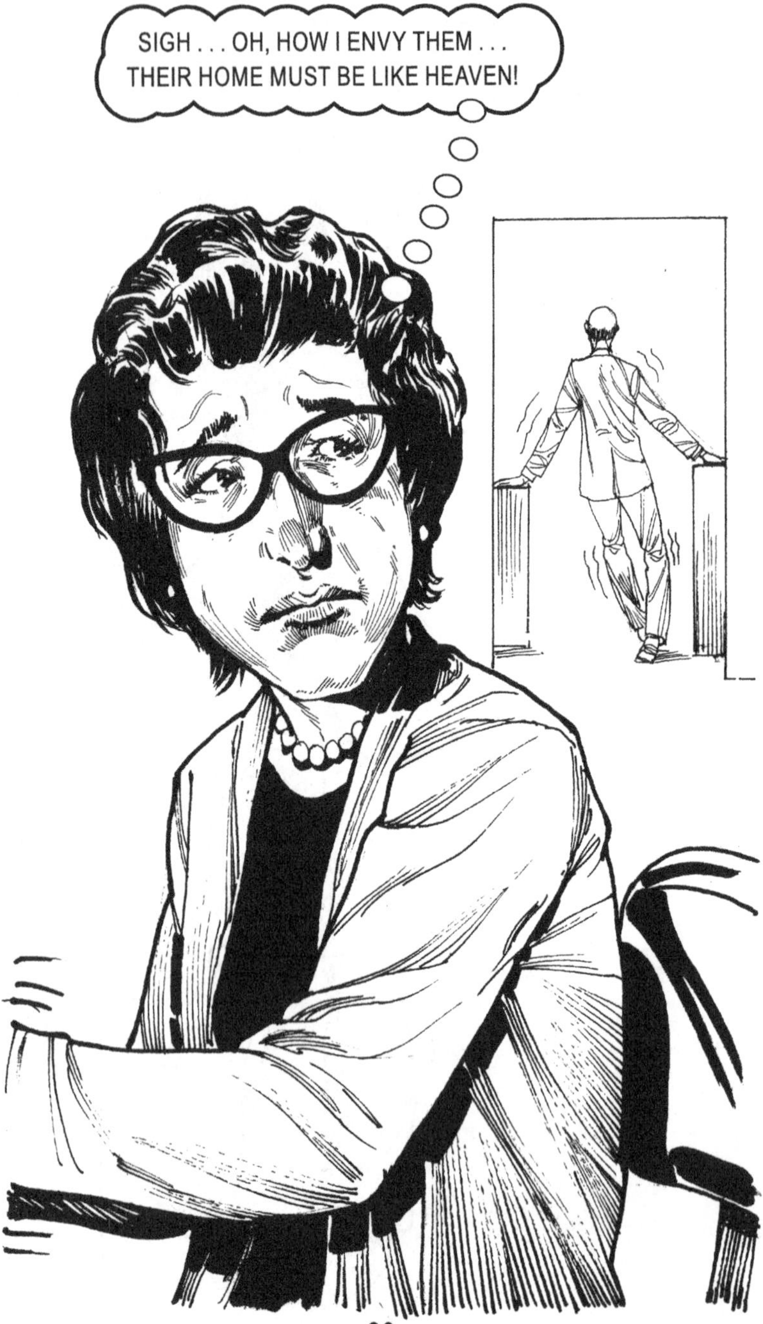
SIGH . . . OH, HOW I ENVY THEM . . .
THEIR HOME MUST BE LIKE HEAVEN!

81

82

83

84

85

MATT. 18:21-22

91

92

DEC. 28TH—MY HEART BEGAN TO BEAT TODAY ALL BY ITSELF. FROM NOW ON IT SHALL GENTLY BEAT FOR THE REST OF MY LIFE WITHOUT EVER STOPPING TO REST! AND AFTER MANY YEARS IT WILL TIRE. IT WILL STOP, AND THEN I SHALL DIE.

JAN. 7TH—I'M GROWING A BIT EVERYDAY. MY ARMS AND LEGS ARE BEGINNING TO TAKE SHAPE. BUT I HAVE TO WAIT A LONG TIME YET BEFORE THOSE LITTLE LEGS WILL RAISE ME TO MY MOTHER'S ARMS, BEFORE THESE LITTLE ARMS WILL BE ABLE TO GATHER FLOWERS AND EMBRACE MY FATHER!

JAN. 16TH—TINY FINGERS ARE BEGINNING TO FORM ON MY HANDS. FUNNY HOW SMALL THEY ARE! I SHALL BE ABLE TO STROKE MY MOTHER'S HAIR WITH THEM AND I SHALL TAKE HER HAIR TO MY MOUTH AND SHE WILL PROBABLY SAY "OH, NO, NO, DEAR!"

JAN. 21ST—IT WASN'T UNTIL TODAY THAT THE DOCTOR TOLD MOM THAT I AM LIVING HERE UNDER HER HEART. OH, MOM, HOW HAPPY SHE MUST BE! ARE YOU HAPPY, MOM?

JAN. 25TH MY MOM AND DAD ARE PROBABLY THINKING ABOUT A NAME FOR ME. BUT THEY DON'T EVEN KNOW THAT I'M A GIRL. THEY ARE PROBABLY SAYING "ANDY." BUT I WANT TO BE CALLED KATHY. I AM GETTING SO BIG ALREADY!

94

FEB. 24TH—I WONDER IF MOM HEARS THE WHISPER OF MY HEART? SOME CHILDREN COME INTO THE WORLD A LITTLE SICK. AND THEN THE DELICATE HANDS OF THE DOCTOR PERFORMS MIRACLES TO BRING THEM TO HEALTH.

IT BEATS SO EVENLY ... TUB ...TUB ... TUB ... YOU HAVE A HEALTHY LITTLE DAUGHTER, MOM!

95

"TIMETABLE FOR MURDER" PRINTED WITH THE PERMISSION OF *THE REMNANT*, VOL. 3, NO. 10, 2539 MORRISON AVE, SAINT PAUL, MINNESOTA 35117

NEXT MORNING
MAMA! I'VE GOT GREAT NEWS! GUESS WHAT?
IT WAS A FALSE ALARM!
(GASP) THANK YOU, DEAR LORD. THANK YOU!

CHAPTER FIVE

UNTIL DEATH US DO PART

NOTE:

THIS CHAPTER DEALS WITH DIVORCE, SOME FAMILIES ARE SO MESSED UP AND ENTANGLED THAT ONLY GOD ALONE CAN SOLVE THE PROBLEM.

100

102

103

105

108

109

110

*PSALM 127:3

*"ALL THINGS WERE MADE BY HIM (JESUS); AND WITHOUT HIM WAS NOT ANYTHING MADE THAT WAS MADE." JOHN 1:3

**"...AND THE GOD (JESUS) IN WHOSE HAND THY BREATH IS..." DANIEL 5:23

***AND THESE WORDS, WHICH I COMMAND THEE THIS DAY, SHALL BE IN THINE HEART: AND THOU SHALL TEACH THEM DILIGENTLY UNTO THY CHILDREN." DEUTERONOMY 6:6,7

114

115

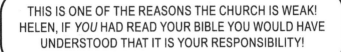

116

117

*AND I SAY UNTO YOU, WHOSOEVER SHALL PUT AWAY HIS WIFE, EXCEPT IT BE FOR FORNICATION, AND SHALL MARRY ANOTHER, COMMITTETH ADULTERY; AND WHOSO MARRIETH HER WHICH IS PUT AWAY DOTH COMMIT ADULTERY. MATTHEW 19:9

121

YOU SEE, PAT, THE BIBLE SAYS "THOU WILT KEEP HIM IN PERFECT PEACE, WHOSE MIND IS STAYED ON THEE:" (ISAIAH 26:3)

LOOK, PAT, EVEN IF YOU BELIEVE YOU ARE RIGHT, GO THE EXTRA MILE AND ASK YOUR HUSBAND TO FORGIVE YOU. GIVE 150% IF HE ONLY GIVES 50%. IF YOU ARE INSULTED, THEN TRY TO TAKE IT GRACIOUSLY.

I KNOW IT'S HARD, BUT GOD WILL HELP YOU. YOU SEE, LOVE IS LONGSUFFERING. (1 CORINTHIANS 13TH CHAPTER)

ANGELS ARE WATCHING. SO IS THE LORD. LEARN TO BITE YOUR TONGUE. BE CONTENT. BE PATIENT. BE GRATEFUL FOR WHAT YOU HAVE.

STOP CRITICIZING. THANK GOD FOR YOUR MATE. IT *COULD* BE MUCH WORSE. NOBODY IS PERFECT, ONLY CHRIST IS PERFECT.

PAT, *DIVORCE IS A COP-OUT!* IF YOU BELIEVE GOD'S WORD, WHERE HUSBANDS SHOULD LOVE THEIR WIVES EVEN AS CHRIST ALSO LOVED THE CHURCH, AND GAVE HIMSELF FOR IT, (EPHESIANS 5:25)

AND YOU SUBMIT, AS INSTRUCTED IN EPHESIANS 5:22-24. IF YOU REALLY DID THAT, SATAN WOULD BE STOPPED COLD!

125

126

ALL THIS DIVORCE IS PART OF PROPHECY.

IT'S A SIGN OF THE END TIMES! AS IT WAS IN THE DAYS OF NOAH, SO SHALL IT BE ALSO WHEN JESUS RETURNS TO THIS EARTH!*

WHAT DOES THAT MEAN?

*BUT AS THE DAYS OF NOAH WERE, SO SHALL ALSO THE COMING OF THE SON OF MAN BE. MATTHEW 24:37

128

129

130

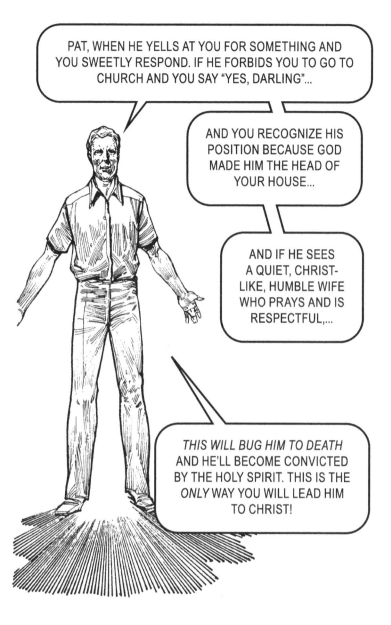

READ 1 PETER 3:1-6

131

133

134

CHAPTER SIX

THE GOOD SAMARITAN

136

137

138

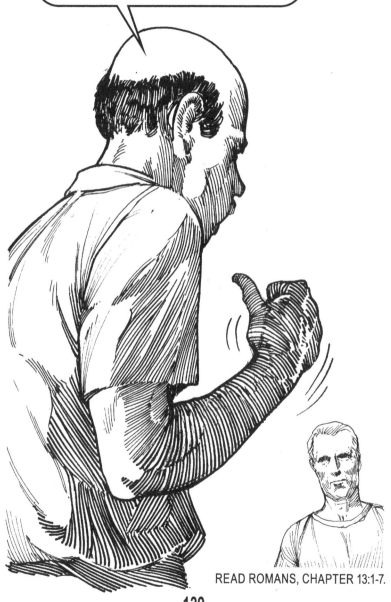

READ ROMANS, CHAPTER 13:1-7.

140

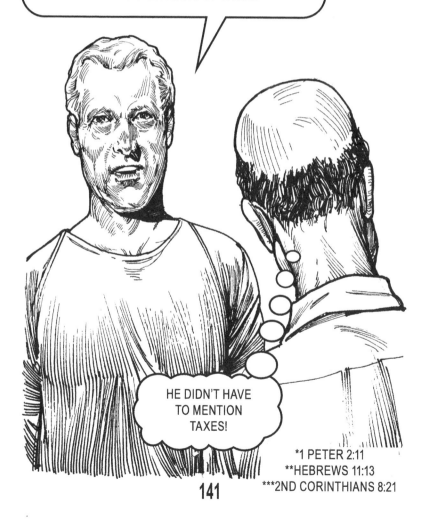

141

143

144

145

*LET YOUR LIGHT SO SHINE BEFORE MEN, THAT THEY
MAY SEE YOUR GOOD WORKS, AND GLORIFY YOUR
FATHER WHICH IS IN HEAVEN. MATTHEW 5:16

146

148

149

150

152

153

154

155

157

I *REALLY* APPRECIATE ALL OF YOUR HELP. YOU WERE A GODSEND.
GOO!
THE LORD SET THIS UP FOR US. HERE'S A LITTLE TRACT I'D LIKE YOU TO READ.
AND A FEW DOLLARS TO HELP YOU AND YOUR HUBBY OUT. GOODBYE. MAY GOD BLESS YOU AND THAT BEAUTIFUL LITTLE BABY OF YOURS!
THIS IS *TOO* MUCH!

160

CHAPTER SEVEN

SHHHHHHH!

162

163

164

165

166

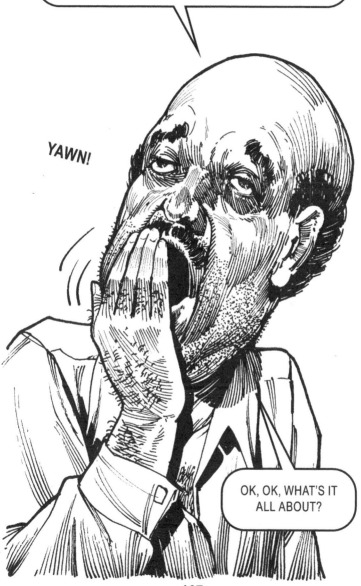

168

169

170

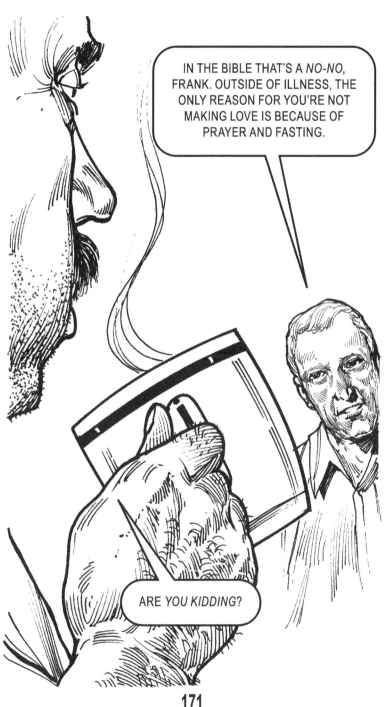

171

172

173

174

175

176

177

178

179

181

*EPHESIANS 5

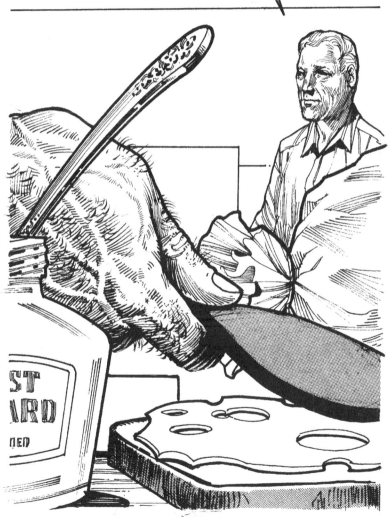

184

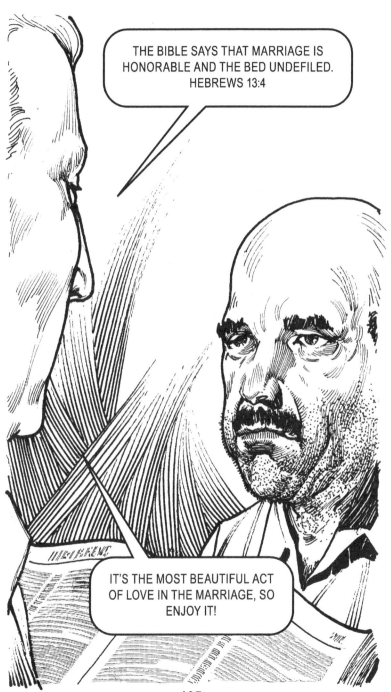

185

THE LOVE ACT DOESN'T END WITH THE CLIMAX FOR EACH PARTNER. A LOVING HUSBAND DOESN'T JUST TURN OVER AND GO TO SLEEP.

HE WILL HOLD HIS WIFE IN HIS ARMS AND TELL HER HOW MUCH HE LOVES HER!

FRANK, DON'T BE AFRAID TO SHOW YOUR AFFECTION FOR HELEN IN PUBLIC!
BURP! ... AHH, THAT WAS GOOD.
HOLD HER HAND OR GIVE HER A KISS AND A SQUEEZE ONCE IN A WHILE. THAT'LL MAKE HER PROUD THAT HER HUSBAND LOVES HER THAT MUCH.
GEE, MARK, I'D FEEL LIKE A NUT.
TRY IT AND SEE IF SHE LIKES IT. I BET SHE WILL!

*PROVERBS 5:18, 19

189

190

191

192

193

194

195

196

197

198

200

WIVES SUBMIT YOURSELVES UNTO YOUR OWN HUSBANDS AS UNTO THE LORD. FOR THE HUSBAND IS THE HEAD OF THE WIFE, EVEN AS CHRIST IS THE HEAD OF THE CHURCH: AND HE IS THE SAVIOUR OF THE BODY. THEREFORE AS THE CHURCH IS SUBJECT UNTO CHRIST, SO LET WIVES BE TO THEIR OWN HUSBANDS IN EVERYTHING. EPHESIANS 5:22-24

203

204

AN EXCELLENT STUDY BOOK FOR MARRIED COUPLES IS:
"INTENDED FOR PLEASURE," BY ED WHEAT MD AND GAYE WHEAT,
FLEMING H REVELL COMPANY.

CHAPTER EIGHT

FAREWELL

211

*EPHESIANS 6:10

213

214

215

217

219

221

WE LOVE YOU, MRS. SMITH, AND SO DOES JESUS. WOULD YOU LIKE TO GO TO CHURCH WITH US NEXT SUNDAY?... AND HAVE DINNER WITH US?
I'D LOVE TO! YOU KNOW SOMETHING?
WHAT, MRS. SMITH?

THE END